Maths

The 11+
10-Minute Tests

For the CEM (Durham University) test

Ages

8-9

Practise • Prepare • Pass

Everything your child needs for 11+ success

How to use this book

This book is made up of 10-minute tests and puzzle pages.
There are answers and detailed explanations in the pull-out section at the back of the book.

10-Minute Tests

- There are 31 tests in this book, each containing 12 questions.

- Each test is designed to cover a good range of the question styles and topics
  that your child could come across in the maths section of their 11+ test.

- Your child should aim to score around 10 or 11 out of 12 in each 10-minute test.
  If they score less than this, use their results to work out the areas they need more practice on.

- If your child hasn't managed to finish the test in time, they need to work on increasing their
  speed, whereas if they have made a lot of mistakes, they need to work more carefully.

- Keep track of your child's scores using the progress chart on the inside back cover of the book.

Puzzle Pages

- There are 12 puzzle pages in this book, which are a great break from test-style questions.
  They encourage children to practise the same skills that they will need in the test,
  but in a fun way.

Published by CGP

Editors:
Emily Forsberg, Sarah Pattison, Hayley Thompson

With thanks to Alison Griffin, Shaun Harrogate and Sharon Keeley-Holden for the proofreading.

Please note that CGP is not associated with CEM or The University of Durham in any way.
This book does not include any official questions and it is not endorsed by CEM or The University of Durham.
CEM, Centre for Evaluation and Monitoring, Durham University and *The University of Durham*
are all trademarks of The University of Durham.

ISBN: 978 1 78294 773 8
Printed by Elanders Ltd, Newcastle upon Tyne
Clipart from Corel®

Based on the classic CGP style created by Richard Parsons.

Contents

Test 1

10

You have **10 minutes** to do this test. Work as quickly and accurately as you can.

1. Cadnam School has nine hundred and seven pupils.
   How is this number written using digits? Circle the correct option.

A	907	**C**	9.7	**E**	970
B	97	**D**	790		

2. Jenna ran 1500 m in a race. How many kilometres did Jenna run?

    km

3. What is 28 in Roman numerals? Circle the correct option.

A	CCVIII	**C**	XXIII	**E**	LXIII
B	XVIII	**D**	XXVIII		

4. What is the missing number in this sum?

   $$5 + 9 - 12 + \underline{\ ?\ } = 17$$

5. A class of children record their eye colours.
   $^1/_4$ of the class have green eyes. $^1/_2$ have blue eyes. The rest have brown eyes.
   What fraction of the class have brown eyes? Circle the correct answer.

   A $^1/_4$
   B $^1/_3$
   C $^1/_2$
   D $^3/_4$
   E $^2/_3$

Test 1   2

A jar contains 1137 jelly beans.
Mahiya takes some of the jelly beans out of the jar.
The bar chart shows how many of each flavour she has taken.

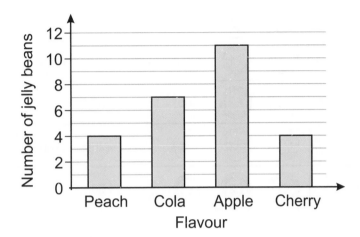

6. How many more cola jelly beans did Mahiya take than cherry jelly beans?

7. How many jelly beans are left in the jar?

The diagram below shows the amounts of red and blue paint to mix to make purple paint.
Each section of the circle represents a fraction of the total amount of paint.

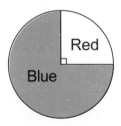

8. How many litres of blue paint are needed to make 8 litres of purple paint?

     litres

9. 12 litres of blue paint are used to make some purple paint.
    How many litres of red paint are used?

    litres

Ben and his friends are counting up their pocket money.
Each of their coins is shown in the table below.

Ben	£2	£1	£1	10p		
Joanna	£1	£1	£1	50p	20p	20p
Parker	£2	£2	50p	50p	50p	10p
Amelia	50p	50p	50p	20p	20p	10p	10p
Haim	£2	£2	£1	£1	50p		

10. Who has saved up the most pocket money? Circle the correct answer.

A   Ben   **C**   Parker   **E**   Haim
B   Joanna   **D**   Amelia

11. Haim wants to buy a DVD that costs £9.99.
How much more money does he need?

£ ☐ . ☐ ☐

12. The shape below was made by joining together two identical triangles.
The perimeter of each triangle is 18 cm and all sides are equal in length.
What is the perimeter of the shape below?

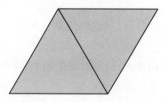

☐ ☐ cm

/ 12

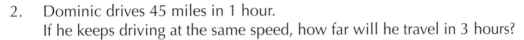

You have **10 minutes** to do this test. Work as quickly and accurately as you can.

1. Farrah and Thomas cut a pie into 10 equal slices.
    Farrah eats $^3/_{10}$ of the pie. Thomas eats $^2/_{10}$ of the pie.
    How many slices are left?

2. Dominic drives 45 miles in 1 hour.
    If he keeps driving at the same speed, how far will he travel in 3 hours?

     miles

3. A grass snake is 120 cm long. How long is the grass snake in metres?
    Circle the correct option.

    A   12 m

    B   1.2 m

    C   1200 m

    D   12 000 m

    E   0.12 m

4. What is the perimeter of the shape below?

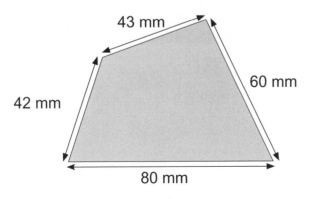

43 mm

60 mm

42 mm

Not drawn
to scale

80 mm

mm

The table below shows the results of every team in a football tournament.
Teams get 2 points for each game they win and 1 point for each game they draw.
1 point is subtracted for each game they lose.

Team	Number of Games		
	Won	Drawn	Lost
A	2	1	1
B	2	1	1
C	0	1	3
D	3	0	1
E	1	1	2

5.   How many points does Team B have?

6.   How many points did Team B beat Team C by?

     A   3   **B**   4   **C**   5   **D**   6   **E**   7

The bar chart shows the ages of the workers at a supermarket.

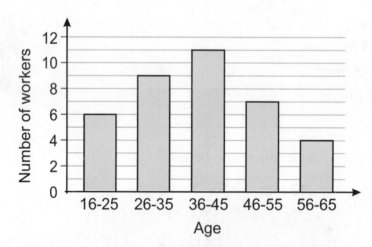

7.   How many workers are 25 years old or younger?

8.   How many workers are at least 46 years old? Circle the correct option.

     A   7   **B**   11   **C**   15   **D**   18   **E**   22

Edward takes his two children to a museum one afternoon.
Edward checks the time when they leave home and when they arrive at the museum.
These times are shown below.

Leave home   Arrive at museum

9.   How many minutes did it take Edward and his family to get to the museum?

 mins

10.   An adult's museum ticket costs £11.50. A child's museum ticket costs £5.20.
      How much will it cost Edward and his two children to enter the museum?

£ [ ][ ].[ ][ ]

Kendra's bar of chocolate is shown on the right.
It weighs 120 g.

11.   She gives Toby ⅓ of the bar.
      How many squares of chocolate did Kendra give Toby?

12.   What is the weight of the chocolate that Kendra has left?

 g

/ 12

You have **10 minutes** to do this test. Work as quickly and accurately as you can.

1. Which pair of lines are parallel to one another?
    Circle the correct option.

    A   B   C   D   E

2. Which of the following shapes is the same as the shape on the right?
    Circle the correct option.

    A   B   C    D   E

Some of the squares in the grid below have been shaded.

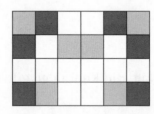

3. What fraction of the grid has been shaded grey? Circle the correct option.

    A $^1/_6$ B $^1/_4$ C $^2/_3$ D $^2/_4$ E $^2/_5$

4. How many more squares need to be shaded blue so that $^1/_3$ of the grid is blue?

Brian records the temperature in his garden. His data is shown on the line graph below.

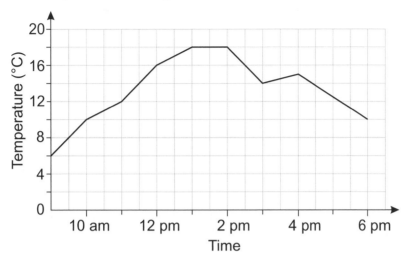

5.   What was the temperature at 12 pm?

 °C

6.   How many degrees warmer was it at 1 pm than at 11 am?

 °C

Nathan and Josie are playing darts on the board on the right. The score for each section is shown on the dartboard.

The black spots show where Nathan's darts landed in the first round.

The white spots show where Josie's darts landed in the first round.

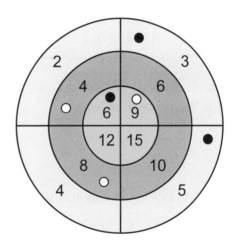

7.   How many points did Nathan score?

8.   In the next round, Josie scored 25 points.
     What is her overall score for the two rounds?

The ingredients below make 12 cupcakes.

110 g butter	1 tsp vanilla extract
110 g sugar	110 g self-raising flour
2 eggs	2 tbsp milk

Paisley wants to make 120 cupcakes for a charity event.

9. How many grams of sugar will Paisley need to make her cupcakes?

 g

10. Eggs come in packs of 6. What is the smallest number of packs Paisley needs to buy?
Circle the correct option.

    A 1   **B** 2   **C** 3   **D** 4   **E** 5

Part of the menu at a fast food restaurant is shown below.

Chicken Nuggets		Drinks	
Box of 6	£2.00	Cola	?
Box of 8	£2.50	Lemonade	£1.45
Box of 12	£3.00	Juice	£1.50

11. Josh buys a box of 12 chicken nuggets, a cola and a juice. The total cost is £6.10.
What is the price of a cola?

£

12. What is the cheapest way to buy 24 chicken nuggets? Circle the correct option.

    A   4 boxes of 6 chicken nuggets.

    B   3 boxes of 8 chicken nuggets.

    C   2 boxes of 12 chicken nuggets.

    D   2 boxes of 6 chicken nuggets and 1 box of 12 chicken nuggets.

    E   Each way costs the same.

/ 12

This puzzle is a great way to practise your **3 times table**. Ready, steady, go!

Monster Maze

There are hungry monsters lurking in the maze.
Monsters holding shields with multiples of 3 on them are vegetarians.
For safe passage through the maze, find a route which only passes the
vegetarian monsters.

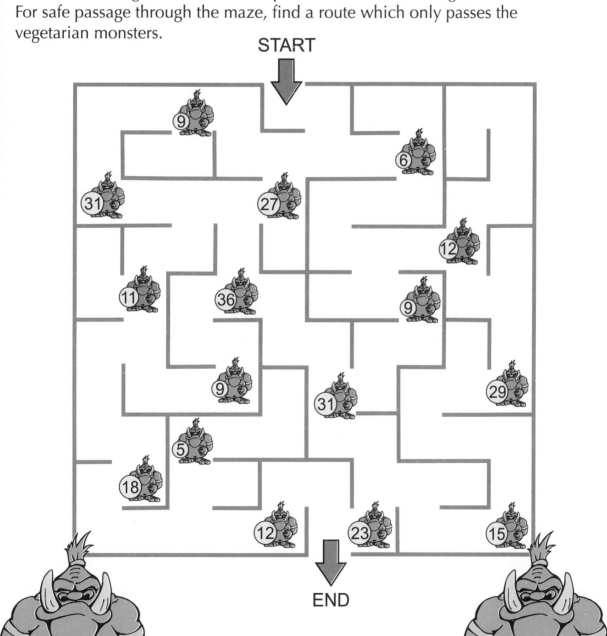

START

END

You have **10 minutes** to do this test. Work as quickly and accurately as you can.

1. A chicken farmer has 820 eggs in incubators. Only half of the eggs hatch. How many eggs hatch?

2. Kabir rounds a number to the nearest 10. The number he rounds to is 110. Which of the following could have been Kabir's original number? Circle the correct option.

   A   104   **B**   115   **C**   99   **D**   113   **E**   123

3. Hazel has 3 cats. Each cat has 4 kittens. Five of the kittens go to new homes. How many cats and kittens does Hazel have left?

4. The grid shows three points of a square labelled A, B and C. Give the coordinates of the point that would complete the square.

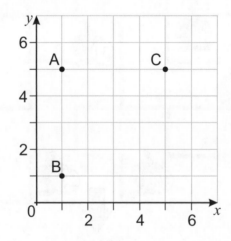

12

On Carol's 30th birthday, she gave birth to Sharon.
On Sharon's 27th birthday, she gave birth to Emily.

5. How old was Carol when Emily was born?

 years old

6. Sharon was born in 1965. In what year was Emily born?

7. Penny is buying some bread, milk and a packet of crisps. The total comes to £4.11. She gives the shopkeeper the following coupons. How much does she have to pay?

£

The different pizzas ordered at a restaurant are shown in the pictogram below.

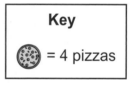

Pepperoni	🍕 🍕 🍕 🍕
Hawaiian	🍕
Spicy Veggie	🍕 🍕 🍕
BBQ Chicken	🍕 🍕

Key

🍕 = 4 pizzas

8. Which of the following statements is true? Circle the correct option.

   A   10 pizzas were ordered in total.
   B   The BBQ Chicken pizza was twice as popular as the Hawaiian pizza.
   C   2 more Spicy Veggie pizzas were ordered than BBQ Chicken pizzas.
   D   13 Pepperoni pizzas were ordered.
   E   An even number of Spicy Veggie pizzas were ordered.

9. Each pizza is cut into 8 slices. How many slices of Hawaiian pizza were ordered?

10. A video game normally costs £20. A shop has a deal on for the games:

GAMES R US

¼ off the price of every game

How much money will Robin save if he uses the deal to buy 3 games?

£ ☐☐

This incomplete sorting diagram shows shapes with an even number of sides and shapes containing only obtuse angles.

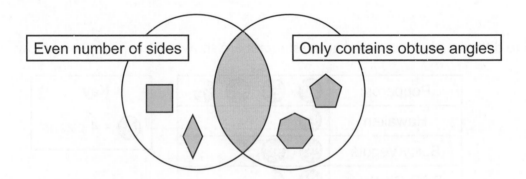

Even number of sides

Only contains obtuse angles

11. Which of the following shapes can be placed in the shaded area of the diagram? Circle the correct option.

A △   B ⬜   C ⬡   D ▭   E ☆

12. Which of the following shapes would not fit in the sorting diagram? Circle the correct option.

A △   B ⬜   C ⬡   D ▭   E ☆

/ 12

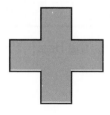

You have **10 minutes** to do this test. Work as quickly and accurately as you can.

1. Which of the following decimals is equivalent to $^1/_2$? Circle the correct option.

    A 0.1   **B** 0.2   **C** 0.25   **D** 0.5   **E** 0.75

2. Leah's hair grows at a rate of 1.25 cm a month.
    How many centimetres will Leah's hair grow in 4 months?

    ☐.☐☐ cm

A screwdriver is measured against a centimetre ruler.

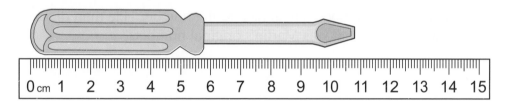

3. How long is the screwdriver?

    ☐☐.☐ cm

4. How many lines of symmetry does this shape have? Circle the correct option.

    A 1   **B** 2   **C** 4   **D** 6   **E** 8

5. Some weights have been put on the set of measuring scales shown below.
    The scales do not balance.

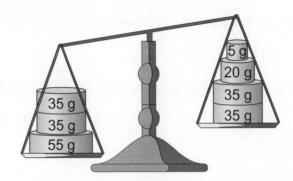

Which of the following could you add to the right-hand side to balance the scales?
Circle the correct option.

A   B   C   D   E

6. Martin thinks of a number. He adds 7 to the number. He then divides it by 3.
    His answer is 12. What was Martin's original number?

The children in a class were given a list of activities and asked which
one they liked best. The results are given in the table below.

Activity	Frequency
Football	IIII
Gymnastics	ꟷꟷꟷꟷꟷ I
Reading	ꟷꟷꟷꟷꟷ II
Horse riding	III
Swimming	ꟷꟷꟷꟷꟷ III

7. How many pupils liked swimming the best?

8. What fraction of the class liked reading the best? Circle the correct answer.

A $^1/_3$ B $^1/_7$ C $^3/_4$ D $^1/_4$ E $^1/_5$

Monica is putting together packets of fudge to sell at a school fair.

9. Monica ties a ribbon around each packet.
    Each packet needs 20 cm of ribbon. Monica needs to make 100 packets.
    How many metres of ribbon will she need?

 m

10. A cube of the fudge is shown on the right.
    What is the perimeter of one face of the cube?

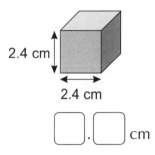

2.4 cm

2.4 cm

.⬜ cm

A point, Q, has been draw on the grid.

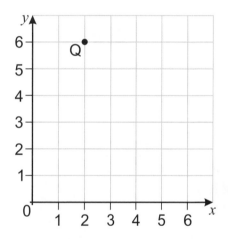

11. A line is drawn on the grid. Point Q sits on this line.
    Which of the following pairs of coordinates could sit at either end of this line?
    Circle the correct option.

    A   (2, 2) and (6, 2)   C   (1, 6) and (5, 6)   E   (6, 1) and (6, 5)
    B   (1, 1) and (4, 1)   D   (3, 1) and (3, 6)

12. Point Q is moved 3 squares to the right and 4 squares down.
    What are the new coordinates of point Q?

    (⬜,⬜)

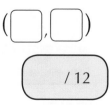

/ 12

Break time! These puzzles are perfect for practising your **number** skills.

Honeycomb Connections

The bees have stored some numbers in the honeycomb.

Draw lines through the empty hexagons to connect the pairs of numbers that add up to 15.

You can only draw 1 line through each hexagon. 1 pair has already been connected for you.

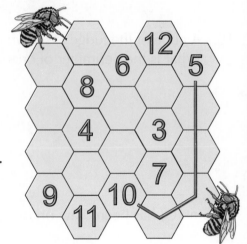

Snaky Sums

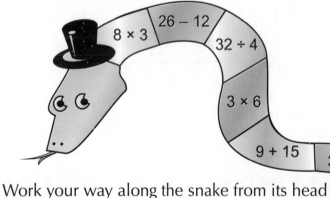

8 × 3   26 – 12   32 ÷ 4   3 × 6   9 + 15   36 – 29   22 ÷ 2   2 × 9   7 + 5

A	B	C	D	E	F	G
18	8	23	5	14	19	6

H	I	J	K	L	M	N
22	11	20	1	26	10	12

O	P	Q	R	S	T	U
15	3	9	16	24	7	21

V	W	X	Y	Z
17	4	25	13	2

Work your way along the snake from its head and find the answers to the calculations. Use your answers and the code to spell out the snake's name.

Answers:									
The snake's name is:									

You have **10 minutes** to do this test. Work as quickly and accurately as you can.

Roger counted the number of pages he read in a book over the weekend.
He drew a pictogram to show his data.

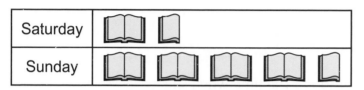

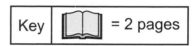

1.   How many pages did Roger read on Sunday?

2.   How many more pages did Roger read on Sunday than on Saturday?

3.   Which of the angles below is obtuse? Circle the correct option.

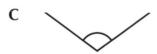

4.   What number is shown by the Roman numeral?
     Circle the correct option.

XXXVI

A	13	**C**	25	**E**	54
B	36	**D**	34		

19   Test 6

5. Mr Bennet wants to divide his class into equally-sized teams for sports day.
    There are 32 students in his class in total.
    Which of the following cannot be a team size? Circle the correct option.

    A   4

    B   2

    C   12

    D   8

    E   16

Tripti leaves her house in the afternoon. The time when she leaves is shown below.

6. What is this time on the 24-hour clock?

7. Tripti returns home at 6:45 pm.
    How many minutes did she spend away from the house?

 minutes

8. Khan cycled home from school.
    The graph below shows the distance he cycled over time.

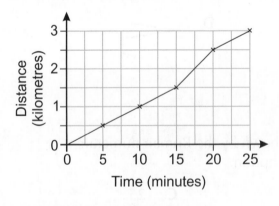

    How far did Khan cycle in the first 15 minutes?

    ⬜.⬜ km

9. The shape below is translated 2 squares to the right and 1 square down. It is then reflected in the mirror line.

What are the coordinates of the new point A?
Circle the correct option.

    A   (11, 5)
    B   (7, 1)
    C   (9, 3)
    D   (4, 12)
    E   (3, 4)

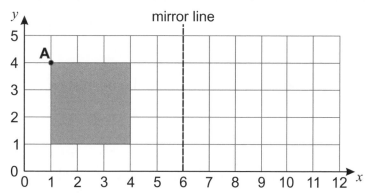

10. Which of the following is the largest amount of money?
Circle the correct option.

    A $\frac{1}{4}$ of £80
    B $\frac{1}{3}$ of £120
    C $\frac{1}{2}$ of £90
    D   Double £17
    E   Triple £12

Gwen has 70 rabbits. $\frac{1}{10}$ of the rabbits have black hair and $\frac{6}{10}$ of the rabbits have brown hair. The rest have white hair.

11. How many of the rabbits have brown hair?

12. How many of the rabbits have white hair?

/ 12

⏱ 10

You have **10 minutes** to do this test. Work as quickly and accurately as you can.

1. A beetle is 4.6 cm long.
   Round this measurement to the nearest cm.

 cm

2. Some squares are shaded on the grid below. What is the smallest number of squares that must be shaded so that the pattern is reflected in the mirror line?

mirror line

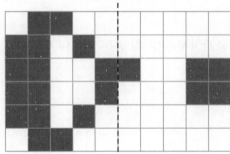

3. Farmer Giles' pigs are shown below.
   What fraction of the pigs are grey?

4. What is $^9/_{25} + ^3/_{25}$? Circle the correct option.

   A $^6/_{25}$ **B** $^{12}/_{50}$ **C** $^6/_{50}$ **D** $^3/_5$ **E** $^{12}/_{25}$

5. Tyson is planting tomato seeds. He has 10 trays that each hold 6 pots. Tyson plants 3 seeds in every pot. How many seeds does he plant in total?

   A   240   **B**   160   **C**   80   **D**   180   **E**   210

6. Dara's favourite television show starts at 6:20 pm. The show is 1 hour and 25 minutes long. What time will it be when the show finishes?

   ⬜⬜:⬜⬜ pm

Hilda counted the number of eggs that her chickens laid each day.
Her data is shown in the bar chart below.

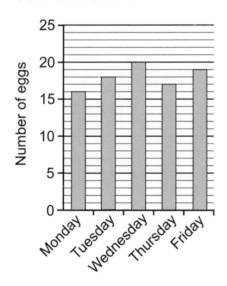

7. How many eggs were laid in total on Monday and Tuesday?

   ⬜⬜

8. How many more eggs were laid on Wednesday than on Thursday?

   ⬜⬜

9. Susan has a watering can containing 5 litres of water. She pours out 355 ml of it.
   How much water is left in the watering can?

      A   4255 ml   **B**   3465 ml   **C**   4645 ml   **D**   825 ml   **E**   3845 ml

10. The shape on the right has
    a perimeter of 20 cm.

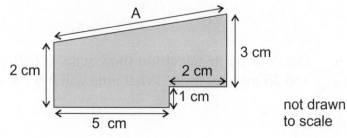

not drawn to scale

    What is the length of side labelled 'A'?

    ☐☐ cm

11. Poppy has a set of tiles that are numbered from 1 to 15. She sorts them into the
    table below. How many tiles should go in the shaded section of the table?

		Factor of 20?	
		Yes	No
Multiple of 4?	Yes		
	No		

    ☐

12. Mrs Dun is taking her class to the crayon museum.
    The table below shows the order form for the tickets.
    What is the price of an adult ticket?

Ticket	Price	Number of Tickets	Total
Child	£5	31	£155
Adult		3	
Senior citizen	£6	1	£6
		Total to pay:	£185

    £ ☐☐

    / 12

You have **10 minutes** to do this test. Work as quickly and accurately as you can.

1. What type of triangle is shown below? Circle the correct option.

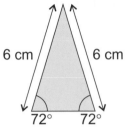

A   isosceles

B   scalene

C   right-angled

D   obtuse

E   equilateral

Candice took a survey in her school. She asked students if they liked gingerbread. Her results are in the table below.

	Yes	No
Boys	卌 卌 卌	卌 卌 |||
Girls	卌 卌 卌 ||||	卌 |||

2. How many students said they didn't like gingerbread? Circle the correct option.

    A   28   C   34   E   27
    B   15   D   21

3. How many more girls than boys like gingerbread?

4. Jenny is thinking of a number.
    She says, "It has six ones, two tens, nine thousands and five hundreds."
    What number is Jenny thinking of?

25

5. Which of the following fractions is equivalent to $^2/_8$?
    Circle the correct option.

    A $^1/_2$ **B** $^3/_4$ **C** $^1/_3$ **D** $^1/_5$ **E** $^1/_4$

6. How long is this eel? Give your answer to the nearest 10 cm.

    [ ][ ] cm

7. The shaded area in the diagram below shows the border around a garden.
    Each square represents 5 m².

    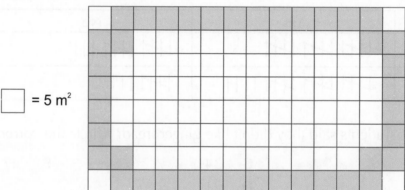

    [ ] = 5 m²

    What is the area of the border?

    [ ][ ][ ] m²

8. Pablo has a bag of 24 sweets.
    He eats $^1/_3$ of the sweets, then divides the rest between his 4 friends.
    How many sweets does each of his friends get?

    [ ]

Rana drives for 35 minutes to get to a concert.
This clock shows the time in the evening that
she arrives at the concert hall.

9.   At what time did she start driving?

 pm

10. The concert starts at quarter to eight.
     How long does Rana have to wait for it to start?

 minutes

Albert wants to go bowling for his birthday.
The prices for the bowling alley are shown below.

Number of Games	Price per Person
1	£6.50
2	£10
3	£14

Menu

Burger   £3

Milkshake   £2

11. How much will it cost in total for Albert and three friends to play 1 game?

£

12. Albert has £100 to spend on games, food and drink for himself and his guests.
     How many people can Albert invite to his birthday if he wants to pay
     for everyone to play two games and have a burger and a milkshake?

/ 12

Puzzles 3

These puzzles are all about **coordinates** and **addition** — go on, get stuck in!

House Hunting

Marty is trying to find Consuela's house using the map below.
She texts him these directions:

From where you are now, go 7 N, 7 E, 6 S, 5 W, 2 N, 4 E, 1 N.

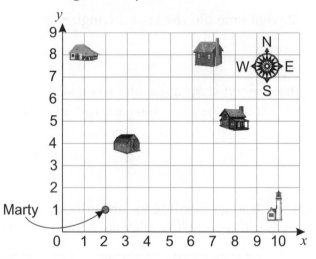

Marty

What are the coordinates of Consuela's house?

Counting Cards

Olive, Byron and Nellie are playing a card game. The aim is to have the hand of cards that has the total closest to 21. Jacks, Queens and Kings are worth 10 points each. The cardholder can decide whether an ace is worth 1 or 11.

Olive

Byron

Nellie

Who's won the game?

You have **10 minutes** to do this test. Work as quickly and accurately as you can.

Jessica has four number cards.

 4   8   5   1

1.   Jessica arranges the cards to make a four digit number.
      What is the largest number she can make?

2.   Which of these statements about the numbers on the cards is true?
      Circle the correct option.

    A   They are all even numbers.

    B   They are all multiples of 2.

    C   If you multiply them all together, you get 180.

    D   They are all factors of 40.

    E   If you multiply them all together, you get an odd number.

Percy reflects the shape below in the mirror line. This makes a new shape.

mirror line

3.   What new shape has he made? Circle the correct option.

A   **B**   **C**   **D**   **E**

4.   How many lines of symmetry does this new shape have?

Jeanette records every pet owned by pupils in Years 3 and 4 in the table below.

	Dog	Cat	Fish	Rabbit	Horse	Hamster
Year 3	5	12	9	8	1	
Year 4	4	7	14	3	2	

5. Which is the most common pet owned by pupils in Years 3 and 4?
    Circle the correct option.

    A Dog   **B** Cat   **C** Fish   **D** Rabbit   **E** Horse

6. The pupils have 72 pets in total. How many of the pets are hamsters?

7. What number is missing from the calculation below?

$$\boxed{2} \times \boxed{?} \times \boxed{6} = \boxed{96}$$

Horace is loading his trailer with 100 empty crates to take back from the market.
Each crate weighs 3.5 kg. When the trailer is empty, it weighs 280 kg.

8. What is the total weight of the trailer and 100 crates?
    Circle the correct option.

    A 630 kg   **C** 35 000 g   **E** 1010 kg
    B 35 280 g   **D** 315 kg

9. On the way to the market, 3 crates fall off the trailer.
    How much lighter will the trailer of crates be?

 kg

10. Michal asked 30 students how they travel to school.
The graph below shows his results.
What fraction of the students travel to school by bus? Circle the correct option.

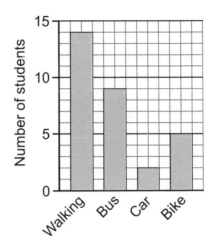

A $^9/_{15}$ B $^8/_{30}$ C $^9/_{10}$ D $^9/_{30}$ E $^8/_{10}$

11. Zabi arranges some rectangles to make the shape below.
What is the perimeter of the shape?

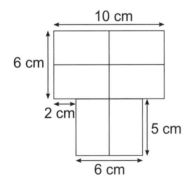

⬜⬜⬜ cm

12. A company normally sells broadband for £24 a month.
Keri uses an offer that gives her $^1/_3$ off the price for 6 months.
How much will she pay in total for broadband for these 6 months?

£⬜⬜⬜

/ 12

You have **10 minutes** to do this test. Work as quickly and accurately as you can.

1. Write $^{27}/_{100}$ as a decimal.

Lydia draws a cross on some grid paper.

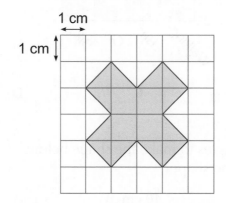

2. How many lines of symmetry does the cross have?

3. What is the area of the cross? Circle the correct option.

   A 8 cm²
   B 10 cm²
   C 12 cm²
   D 14 cm²
   E 16 cm²

4. 3 packets of biscuits contain 21 biscuits altogether.
   How many biscuits will 9 packets contain?

5. Kai has a box of paperclips.
    Each paperclip is 8 mm wide.
    He arranges nine paperclips in a line, as shown.
    How long is the line in centimetres?

8 mm

⬜.⬜ cm

Amir recorded how many cupcakes his bakery sold each day during the week.

Day	Monday	Tuesday	Wednesday	Thursday	Friday
Number of cupcakes	40	59	15	32	29

6. How many cupcakes did the bakery sell in total that week?
    Circle the correct option.

    A   100   **B**   125   **C**   175   **D**   200   **E**   225

7. Amir makes a pictogram to display his data. He uses one circle to represent
    4 cupcakes. Which of the following shows the pictogram for Wednesday?
    Circle the correct option.

8. Chelsea makes 3 pizzas. She slices them as shown below.

pepperoni

chicken

mushroom

    Her friends eat 6 slices of pepperoni pizza, 7 slices of chicken pizza and 4 slices of
    mushroom pizza. What fraction of the three pizzas is left? Circle the correct option.

    A $^6/_{24}$ **B** $^7/_{22}$ **C** $^7/_{24}$ **D** $^8/_{24}$ **E** $^8/_{22}$

9. Which of the following sentences describes the shape on the right?
Circle the correct option.

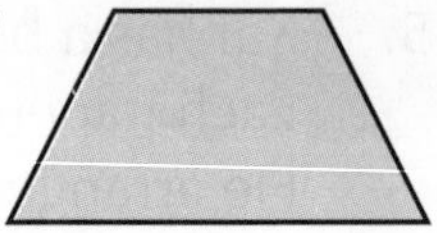

    A   It has 2 pairs of parallel sides.

    B   It has 1 pair of parallel sides and 2 obtuse angles.

    C   It has 2 pairs of perpendicular sides.

    D   It has 4 acute angles.

    E   It has 1 pair of perpendicular sides and 2 acute angles.

Some prices at a grocery shop are shown below.

Apple	Cucumber
60p	80p

10. Kim is buying cucumbers for a salad. She has £5.00.
What is the greatest number of cucumbers she can buy?

11. The grocery shop has an offer on apples:
"Buy 2 apples and get a third apple half price."
Yousaf is buying 6 apples. How much does he have to pay?

£ ☐☐.☐☐

12. Jake takes a taxi to the airport. The price of the taxi is £3.60 plus 25p for every
minute it takes to get to the airport. It takes 40 minutes to get to the airport.
How much does the taxi cost?

£ ☐☐.☐☐

/ 12

Puzzles 4

This puzzle is perfect for practising your **number** and **shape** skills.

Lily Pad Path

Francis the frog needs to hop across the pond using the lily pads.
Each lily pad he hops on should have a value of 1 more than the previous pad.

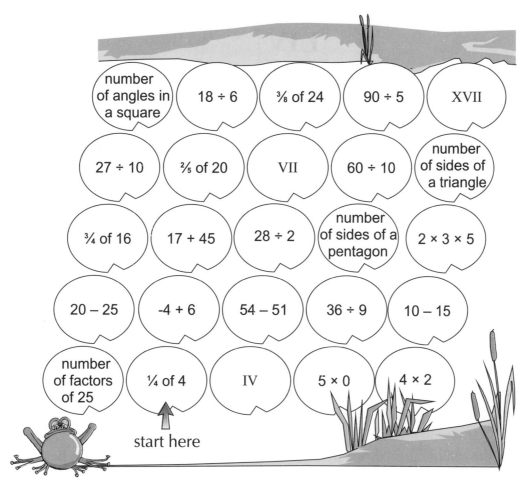

Francis can hop forwards, backwards, left, right and diagonally.
How many lily pads does he have to hop on to get across the pond?

_____

You have **10 minutes** to do this test. Work as quickly and accurately as you can.

1. There are 9567 sweets in a jar.
    How many sweets are there to the nearest 1000?

2. What number does the Roman numeral below show? Circle the correct option.

    LIV

    A   104

    B   54

    C   56

    D   106

    E   504

3. The thermometer below shows the temperature on a cold afternoon in winter.

    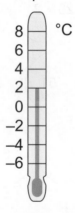

    Later on, the temperature drops by 6 °C. What will the new temperature be?

    $-$ ☐ °C

4. Aarav's sunflower is 1.5 m tall. Amelia's sunflower is 61 cm taller.
    How tall is Amelia's sunflower? Give your answer in cm.

    ☐☐☐ cm

36

5. What fraction of the following angles are acute?

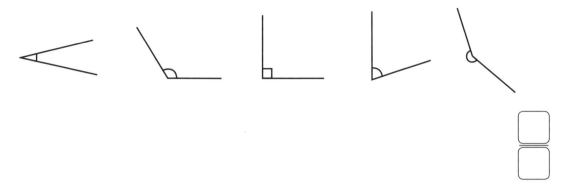

Mia is a singing teacher.
The table shows how many singing lessons she gives each day for five days.

	Mon	Tues	Wed	Thurs	Fri
Number of lessons	3	3	4	5	6

On the days shown above, Mia charges £31.50 per singing lesson.

6. How much money does Mia make on Monday?

£ ☐☐.☐☐

7. On Saturdays, Mia charges £40 per lesson.
   On one Saturday, she makes £120.
   How many singing lessons does Mia give that Saturday?

   ☐

8. Michael is travelling by train from London to Glasgow. The journey takes 4 ½ hours. Michael's train leaves London at 14:07. What time does he arrive in Glasgow? Circle the correct option.

   A 18:07

   B 18:22

   C 18:37

   D 18:52

   E 19:07

The bar chart shows the number of cruises sold by a travel agency during the first 5 months of the year.

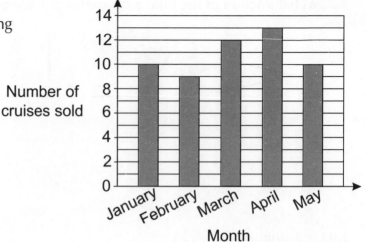

9. The travel agency has a sales target of at least 10 cruises per month.
    During which month did the travel agency not meet its sales target?
    Circle the correct option.

    A January   **B** February   **C** March   **D** April   **E** May

10. How many more cruises were sold in April than May?

11. How many cruises did the travel agency sell in total between January and May?

12. The large rectangle shown below is made up of 9 smaller rectangles.
    What is the perimeter of the large rectangle?

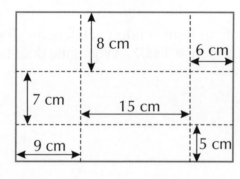

not to scale

cm

/ 12

(10)

You have **10 minutes** to do this test. Work as quickly and accurately as you can.

1. A number sequence is shown below.

    | 30, | 36, | ? | 48, | 54 |

    What is the missing number in the sequence? Circle the correct option.

    A 38
    B 40
    C 42
    D 44
    E 46

Saabiq finishes school at 15:10. He starts band practice at 16:25.

2. What time is 16:25 in the 12-hour clock?

    ☐:☐☐ pm

3. How much time does Saabiq have between the end of school
    and the start of band practice? Give your answer in minutes.

    ☐☐ minutes

4. A cup can hold $\frac{1}{8}$ of a bottle of lemonade.
    Jessica and Celine have 1 cup of lemonade each. Toby has 3 cups of lemonade.
    How many glasses can be filled from the lemonade remaining in the bottle?

    ☐

The pictogram shows the number of books in different categories borrowed from a school library in one day.

Romance	
Horror	
Adventure	
Mystery	

Key: = 2 books

5.   How many books were borrowed from the Romance and Mystery categories in total?

6.   What fraction of the borrowed books were from the Adventure category?
     Circle the correct option.

     A $^1/_4$ **B** $^1/_5$ **C** $^3/_8$ **D** $^5/_{12}$ **E** $^5/_{16}$

7.   Which of these is false? Circle the correct option.
     A $4.2 > 4.1$
     B $3.46 < 3.48$
     C $^1/_4 < 0.35$
     D $0.4 > ^1/_2$
     E $^3/_4 = 0.75$

8.   A recipe needs 2 tablespoons of milk. 1 tablespoon is about 17.8 ml.
     According to the recipe, how much milk is needed to the nearest millimetre?
     Circle the correct option.

     A   17 ml
     B   18 ml
     C   34 ml
     D   36 ml
     E   38 ml

Point X is marked on the grid.

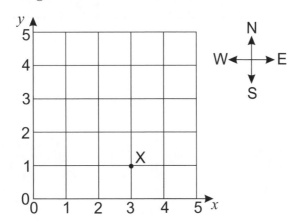

9.   A robot is at point X on the grid. What are its coordinates?

(⬚ , ⬚)

10. The robot is instructed to move 3 squares north from point X, then 2 squares east.
     What are the final coordinates of the robot?

(⬚ , ⬚)

Some prices at a cinema are shown on the right.

Adult ticket: £7.60
Child ticket: £5.40

Small popcorn: £3.25
Large popcorn: £5.75

11. Cleo buys a child ticket and a small popcorn.
     She pays with a £10 note. How much change should she get?

£ ⬚⬚ . ⬚⬚

12. The cinema also offers a family ticket costing £22.
     How much could a family with 2 adults and 2 children save by buying
     the family ticket instead of individual tickets?

£ ⬚⬚ . ⬚⬚

/ 12

You have **10 minutes** to do this test. Work as quickly and accurately as you can.

1. Which of these shapes is a heptagon? Circle the correct option.

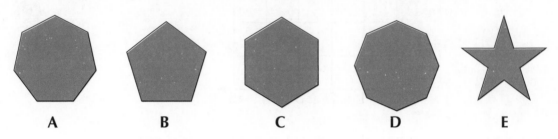

A   B   C   D   E

Kaylee draws this timeline for her project on Queen Victoria.

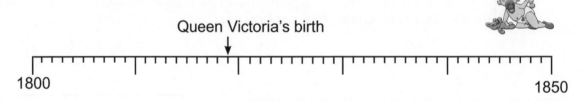

Queen Victoria's birth

1800   1850

2. In what year was Queen Victoria born?

3. Queen Victoria became queen in 1837.
    How many years after she was born did she become queen?

4. Alyssa is 20 minutes late for an afternoon appointment.
    Her watch is shown on the right.
    What time was Alyssa's appointment? Circle the correct option.

A	2:55 pm	C	14:40	E	14:45
B	14:55	D	2.50 pm		

       42

The graph below shows how the speed of Rajani's car changed on her journey to work. Measurements were taken every 5 minutes.

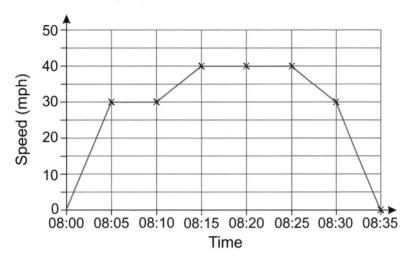

5. At 08:10, how fast was Rajani's car travelling?

    $\boxed{}$ mph

6. In which of the following time periods did the speed of Rajani's car stay the same? Circle the correct option.

    A   08:00 to 08:10
    B   08:05 to 08:15
    C   08:10 to 08:20
    D   08:15 to 08:25
    E   08:20 to 08:30

Jo is making up 50 gift bags to sell in her shop.
She puts 2 bath bombs and 3 soaps into each gift bag.

7. Jo has 136 soaps.
    How many more soaps does Jo need to fill all the gift bags?

8. Jo has 119 bath bombs.
    How many bath bombs will she have left over once she has filled all the gift bags?

Test 13

9. Shape Y on the grid is a translation of shape X.
Which of these correctly describes the translation?
Circle the correct option.

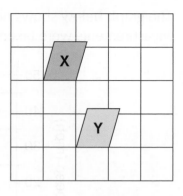

A   1 square right, 2 squares down

B   1 square left, 2 squares down

C   2 squares right, 1 square down

D   2 squares right, 2 squares down

E   3 squares right, 1 square down

10. Jack and Ania are reading the same book.
Jack has just finished Chapter XVI. Ania has just finished Chapter VIII.
How many more chapters has Jack read than Ania? Circle the correct option.

   A   3   B   5   C   8   D   10   E   13

11. The plan for a children's playground is shown
by the shaded squares on the grid. Each
square on the grid measures 1 m by 1 m.

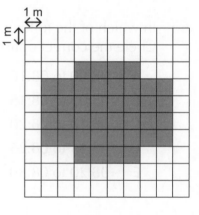

The council wants to put up a fence around the
perimeter of the playground. They need to leave gaps
in the fence for 2 gates. Each gate will be 1.5 m long.
How long will the fence be in total?

☐☐ m

12. A box of paper clips contains 5 large paper clips and 12 small paper clips.
Jan buys enough boxes to have 60 large paper clips.
How many small paper clips does she have?

☐☐☐

/ 12

Puzzles 5

More puzzles! These will let you try out your **problem-solving** skills.

Forgetful Gwen

Gwen has forgotten the ages of her nieces and nephews.
Use the clues below to work out how old each one is.

- Dylan's age is $2 \times 3 \times 4$.
- Layla is 7 times older than Brian.
- Lucy is half of Layla's age, plus 2.
- Brian is Dylan's age divided by 12.

Dylan is _____ years old.   Lucy is _____ years old.

Layla is _____ years old.   Brian is _____ years old.

Puzzling Pigs

Farmer Pigwhistle has numbered each of her pigs with a factor of 24 or 30.
Each pig has a different number.

Farmer Pigwhistle has put her pigs into the pens below. Some of the
pigs have ended up in the wrong pen. One pig has gone missing.

Factors of 30	Factors of both 24 and 30	Factors of 24
10 4	2 3	24
30 5	8 6	1 12

Circle the pigs that have ended up in the wrong pen.

What is the number of the missing pig? _____

You have **10 minutes** to do this test. Work as quickly and accurately as you can.

1. Daniel is sorting buttons. He arranges the buttons in piles of 5.
    He has 9 piles in total. How many buttons does he have?

2. Which of these measurements is nearest to 10 cm? Circle the correct option.

    A   9.8 cm
    B   10.4 cm
    C   9.7 cm
    D   9.6 cm
    E   10.3 cm

3. Max's bank statement says he has –£15 in his bank account. He puts £20 in it.
    How much money does he now have in his account?

    £ ⬚⬚

4. What is the sum of all the even numbers on this clock face?

5. Sophie has a coffee pot that holds 1.8 litres of coffee.
    Each of her cups holds 300 ml.
    How many cups of coffee can Sophie make from 1 full coffee pot?

Jon draws a diagram to show the number of each type of pie he sold in his bakery in one day. Each section of the circle represents a fraction of the total amount.

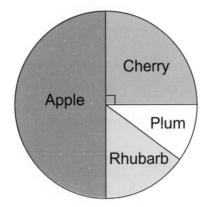

6. Which flavour of pie sold least well? Circle the correct option.

    A Apple   **C** Plum   **E** Cannot tell
    B Rhubarb   **D** Cherry

7. Jon sold 44 pies in total. How many of those were cherry?

Jess draws the shape below. Each square has an area of 1 cm².

mirror line

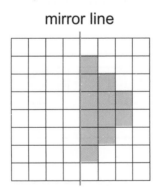

8. Jess reflects the shape in the mirror line.
    What will the total area of the new shape be?

    [ ][ ] cm²

9. How many lines of symmetry will the new shape have? Circle the correct option.

    A 1   **C** 3   **E** 5
    B 2   **D** 4

10. Shabnam has £5 worth of 10p coins in 1 bag.
    She has £5 worth of 2p coins in the another bag.
    How many coins does Shabnam have in total?

11. Some prices for a parcel firm are shown below.

Weight of parcel	Price to send
less than 1.5 kg	£3.00
1.5 to 2.9 kg	£3.45
3.0 to 4.9 kg	£3.85

Harry has 100 DVDs. He wraps them up to make a parcel.
Each DVD weighs 16 g. How much will it cost Harry to send his parcel?

12. The diagram below shows how 3 identical desks are arranged in an office.

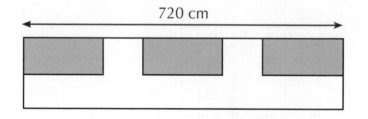

Neighbouring desks are kept an equal distance apart.
What is the distance between the desks?

☐☐ cm

/ 12

© CGP — not to be photocopied

You have **10 minutes** to do this test. Work as quickly and accurately as you can.

1. Emma is 9 years and 5 months old. How old is she in months?

    ⬚⬚⬚ months

2. Milo is thinking of a shape. He says: "My shape has 4 sides.
    It has two pairs of equal-length sides. None of the sides are parallel."
    Which of these is the shape Milo is thinking of? Circle the correct option.

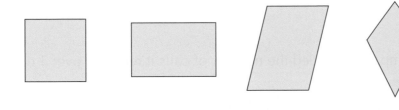

    A   **B**   **C**   **D**   **E**

3. A playing field is shown below.

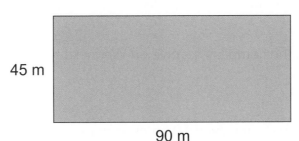

    45 m   Not to scale.

    90 m

    What is the perimeter of the playing field?

    ⬚⬚⬚ m

4. There are 30 children in Stefan's class. $^3/_5$ are boys.
    How many girls are there in Stefan's class?

    ⬚⬚

5. The dial on a safe is shown below.

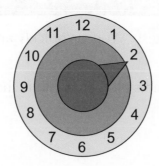

Tim must turn the dial two quarter turns clockwise to open the safe.
What number should the dial end up on?

A computer software company recorded the number of calls it received over 3 days.

Day	Number of calls
Monday	64
Tuesday	53
Wednesday	
Total	190

6. How many calls did the company receive on Wednesday?

7. On Monday, the company received 10 times as many emails as calls.
How many emails did the company receive?

8. Tara buys 5 shepherd's pie ready meals. In total, the meals weigh 2 kg.
How much does one shepherd's pie ready meal weigh?

g

9. The ? represents a number in the statement below.
    Which number does it represent? Circle the correct option.

    $$\frac{1}{5} \text{ of } 30 = ? \text{ of } 24$$

    A $\frac{1}{2}$
    B $\frac{1}{3}$
    C $\frac{1}{4}$
    D $\frac{1}{6}$
    E $\frac{1}{8}$

The distance between New York and London is 5585 km.

10. What is the distance between New York and London in m?
    Circle the correct option.

    A   5.585 m
    B   55.85 m
    C   55 850 m
    D   558 500 m
    E   5 585 000 m

The time in New York is 5 hours behind the time in London.

11. If it is 14:20 in London, what time is it in New York?
    Give your answer using the 24-hour clock.

12. Josh is in London. It is 9:15 am.
    He wants to ring his uncle in New York.
    Josh must wait until it is 8 am in New York before he can ring.

    How long does Josh have to wait before he can ring his uncle?

    ☐ hours and ☐☐ minutes

    / 12

Phew. Puzzle time. This one will help you to practise **directions**.

Monster Mayhem

Jacob is in the park, playing a game on his phone.
The aim of the game is to find and collect monsters.

The dots on the grid show where the monsters are located in the park.
The directions tell Jacob how to find the monsters.

1. Stand at **X** facing **north**.

2. Move forward **1** square.

3. Make $^1/_4$ **turn clockwise**.
   Move forward **3** squares.

4. Make $^1/_2$ **turn anticlockwise**.
   Move forward **2** squares.

5. Turn to face **north**.
   Move forward **4** squares.

6. Make $^1/_4$ **turn clockwise**.
   Move forward **5** squares.

7. Turn to face **north**.
   Move forward **2** squares.

8. Make $^1/_2$ **turn clockwise**.
   Move forward **4** squares.

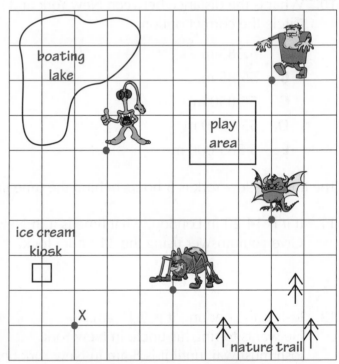

Follow the directions to help Jacob find the monsters.

Draw the route Jacob should take on the grid above.

You have **10 minutes** to do this test. Work as quickly and accurately as you can.

1.　Which of the following numbers is the largest? Circle the correct option.

　　A　887.2

　　B　1028.6

　　C　99.8

　　D　675.4

　　E　8.9

Tasmin measures the height of her bean plant every day.
Her data is shown in the graph below.

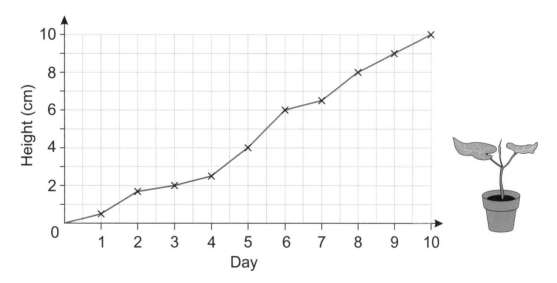

2.　How tall was the bean plant on day 9?

　　　　　　cm

3.　On which day was the bean plant 6.5 cm? Circle the correct option.

　　A　Day 3　　　**B**　Day 4　　　**C**　Day 5　　　**D**　Day 6　　　**E**　Day 7

　　　　　　　53

4. Scarlett buys an 820 ml bottle of washing up liquid.
    After a few weeks, she has used 460 ml.
    How much washing up liquid is left in the bottle?

 ml

Amal and her friends go to a concert.

5. Before the concert, Amal buys a T-shirt for £19.59 and a poster for £11.75.
    How much money does Amal spend?

£ ⬜⬜.⬜⬜

6. Two bands play at the concert. The first band plays for 35 minutes.
    There is then a 20 minute break. The second band plays for 1 hour.
    How long did the concert last in total? Circle the correct option.

    A   110 minutes   **C**   120 minutes   **E**   130 minutes
    B   115 minutes   **D**   125 minutes

7. Ola asks her classmates what their favourite snack is.
    She records the results in this table.

Favourite snack	Number of classmates
Biscuits	18
Chocolate	?
Crisps	6
Fruit	3
Total:	36

    How many of her classmates said their favourite snack was chocolate?
    Circle the correct option.

    A 7   **C** 9   **E** 11
    B 8   **D** 10

8. The grid on the right represents a school dance studio. The shaded squares represent the stage. What fraction of the dance studio is taken up by the stage? Circle the correct option.

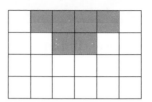

A $^1/_2$ C $^1/_6$ E $^1/_8$

B $^1/_4$ D $^1/_7$

Pat is buying some toilet roll. 1 pack contains 9 rolls.

9. Each roll has 200 sheets. How many sheets of toilet roll come in 1 pack?

10. Each pack costs £7.20. How much does 1 roll cost?

£

Owen and Christina are playing a game with dice.
Each face of a single dice shows a different number of dots between 1 and 6.
Owen rolls the 5 dice shown below.

Owen scores the number of points written on the top face of each dice.
Christina scores the number of points written on the bottom face.

The number of dots on opposite faces of the dice add up to 7.

11. How many points did Christina score?

12. What do all of the dots on a single dice add up to?

/ 12

You have **10 minutes** to do this test. Work as quickly and accurately as you can.

Neville is climbing a mountain. The mountain is 3798 m tall.

1. How tall is the mountain to the nearest 1000 metres?

    [ ][ ][ ][ ] m

2. A hill is $^1/_{10}$ of the height of the mountain Neville climbed.
    How tall is the hill?

    [ ][ ][ ].[ ] m

Jason recorded the amount of rain that fell in his town every month for a year.
His data is shown in the graph below.

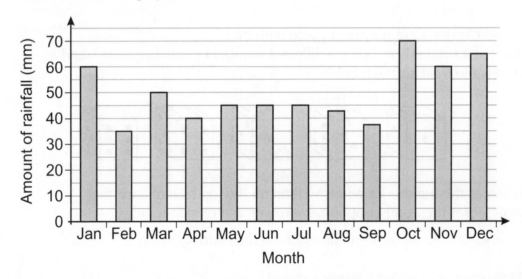

3. In which month did the least rain fall? Circle the correct option.

    A February   **C** June   **E** September

    B April   **D** August

4. How much rain fell in the first 3 months of the year?

    [ ][ ][ ] mm

Savannah has a rectangular piece of paper shown below.

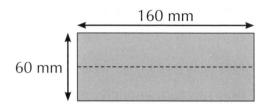

5.   What is the perimeter of the piece of paper?

 mm

6.   She cuts the paper in half along the dotted line and throws 1 piece away.
     What is the perimeter of the remaining piece of paper?

[   ][   ][   ] mm

7.   A kite with corners labelled F and G has been drawn in the grid below.
     The kite is translated 2 squares down and 3 squares to the left.
     What are the new coordinates of F and G?
     Circle the correct option.

     A   (3, 3) and (3, 0).
     B   (2, 6) and (2, 3).
     C   (2, 4) and (2, 1).
     D   (5, 4) and (5, 1).
     E   (4, 5) and (4, 2).

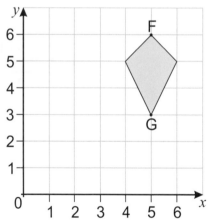

8.   54 pupils and 7 teachers are going on a school trip to a museum.
     The school minibuses have 16 seats each.
     What is the smallest number of minibuses that will be needed for the trip?

[   ]

Asher earns £7.10 an hour.

9. Asher has earned £28.40 in total. How many hours has he been working?

     hours

10. Asher has to work exactly 7 hours to earn enough money to afford a new jacket.
    What is the price of the jacket? Circle the correct option.

    A £37.70   **B** £47.70   **C** £49.70   **D** £35.70   **E** £56.70

5 teams took part in a quiz. Each correct answer to a question scored 1 point.
The team with the most points won. The bar chart below shows the quiz results.

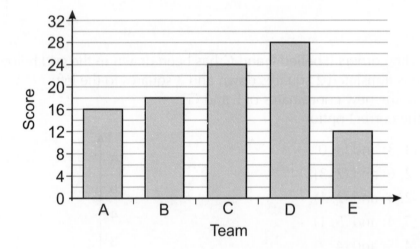

11. By how many points did the winning team beat the team that came last?

12. The quiz was made up of 4 rounds. Team D scored 4 marks in the first round.
    They scored $\frac{1}{2}$ of their total marks in the second round and $\frac{1}{4}$ in the third round.
    How many points did they score in the final round?

/ 12

You have **10 minutes** to do this test. Work as quickly and accurately as you can.

Margaret is making a tomato pasta salad.

1. She has 6 tomatoes. She chops each tomato into eighths.
    How many pieces of tomato are in her salad?

2. Margaret has a 500 g packet of pasta.
    She pours out 280 g of pasta.
    How many grams of pasta will be left in the packet?

A bus company runs buses to and from a town centre.

3. There are 44 people on a bus going to the town centre.
    At the next stop, $^1/_2$ of the people get off the bus and another 16 get on.
    How many people are now on the bus?

4. A different bus is travelling back from the town centre. It stops at a bus stop.
    19 people get off and 14 people get on. There are now 52 people on the bus.
    How many people were on this bus before it stopped? Circle the correct option.

    A   47
    B   71
    C   57
    D   66
    E   31

5. Shape Y is a symmetrical shape.
    Half of shape Y and the line of symmetry are shown below.

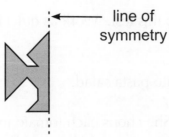

line of
symmetry

Which of the following is the other half of shape Y?
Circle the correct option.

A   B   C   D   E

Students of Bumblebank School are voting for a school president in an election.
The results of the election are shown below.

Election Results	
Percy	307 votes
Alicia	365 votes
Stacey	192 votes

6. What was the total number of votes?

7. How many more votes did Alicia get than Stacey?

8. Alice can do 6 sit-ups in 20 seconds.
    How many sit-ups can she do in 1 minute?

The bar chart below shows how many patients 5 doctors saw before their lunch break.

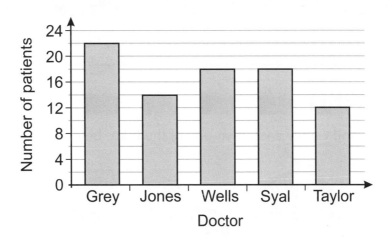

9. How many patients were seen in total by Dr. Grey and Dr. Syal?

10. Dr. Wells spent 10 minutes with each patient.
    How many hours did she spend with her patients in total?

hours

11. Dr. Jones saw 34 patients in total for the whole day.
    How many people did Dr. Jones see after his lunch break?

12. James has 5 different volumes of water. He arranges them in order of size,
    from smallest to largest. Which of these lists shows the correct order?
    Circle the correct option.

    A 1200 ml   12 ml   0.12 L   1.2 ml   12 L
    B 1.2 ml   12 ml   0.12 L   1200 ml   12 L
    C 0.12 L   1.2 ml   12 ml   12 L   1200 ml
    D 1.2 ml   12 ml   0.12 L   12 L   1200 ml
    E 1.2 ml   12 ml   1200 ml   0.12 L   12 L

/ 12

Puzzles 7

Have a go at the puzzles below — they're great for practising your problem-solving skills.

Really Wheely

Regina, Fred, Steve and Carley each own one of the bikes below.

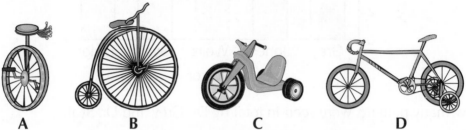

A   **B**   **C**   **D**

Regina says, *"My bike has the most wheels."*
Fred says, *"My bike has 1 wheel less than Steve's bike."*
Steve says, *"My bike has the same number of wheels as the number of sides of a hexagon, minus the number of sides of a trapezium."*

Use the information above work out who owns which bike.
Write the correct letter next to each name.

Regina ☐   Fred ☐   Steve ☐   Carley ☐

Packing Parcels

Percy the postman is getting ready to deliver the morning post.
Help Percy fit the parcels at the back of his van by drawing the parcel outlines below.
Make sure you keep the fragile parcels the right way up!

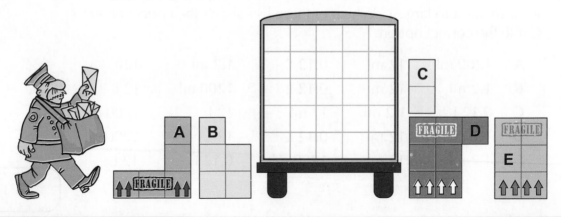

You have **10 minutes** to do this test. Work as quickly and accurately as you can.

1. Johnny is thinking of a shape. The shape has 1 line of symmetry.
    Which of these shapes could Johnny be thinking of? Circle the correct option.

A   B    C   D   E

2. Zac and Gabriella walk from the same point in opposite directions.
    Zac walks 98 m and Gabriella walks 119 m. How far away from Zac is Gabriella?

⬚⬚⬚ m

Philip sells 4 different flavours of milkshake in his cafe.
He records the number of each flavour sold in one day in this pictogram.

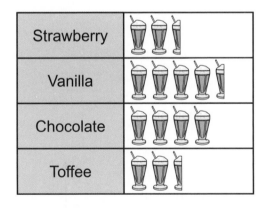

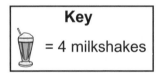

3. How many milkshakes has Philip sold in total?

⬚⬚

4. It costs Philip 80p to make one toffee milkshake.
    He sells each toffee milkshake for £2.20.
    How much money does Philip earn by selling one toffee milkshake?

£⬚.⬚⬚

5. Belle's Victoria sponge has been baking for quarter of an hour.
   The recipe says it needs to bake for a total of 24 minutes.
   How many more minutes does Belle's Victoria sponge need to bake?

 minutes

Callie makes a 3D shape from modelling clay.
Her shape is shown on the right.

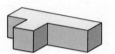

6. How many faces does the 3D shape have?

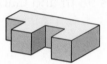

Callie adds some more modelling clay to make the shape
shown on the right.

7. How many more faces does Callie's new shape have compared to her
   original shape? Circle the correct option.

   A 1
   B 2
   C 3
   D 4
   E 5

8. The grid shows 3 points, P, Q and R.

   Which of the following pairs of translations will
   move from point P to point Q and then from
   point Q to point R? Circle the correct option.

   A 4 right and 3 down, then 2 right and 7 up.
   B 5 right and 4 up, then 2 left and 7 down.
   C 5 left and 4 down, then 3 right and 3 down.
   D 5 right and 4 up, then 5 left and 4 down.
   E 4 right and 5 up, then 2 left and 7 down.

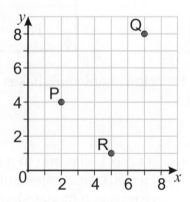

John is making cheese and lettuce sandwiches for a buffet.
He puts the filling between 2 slices of bread.
He then cuts this into quarters to make 4 triangle sandwiches.

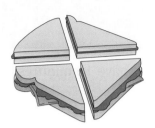

9.   How many slices of bread does he need to make 48 triangle sandwiches?

10.   The cheese costs £5.50 per kilogram. How much would 100 g of cheese cost?
      Give your answer in pence.

 p

Jamal counted the number of each type of minibeast he found in his garden.
His data is shown in the diagram below.
Each section of the circle represents a fraction of the total number of minibeasts.

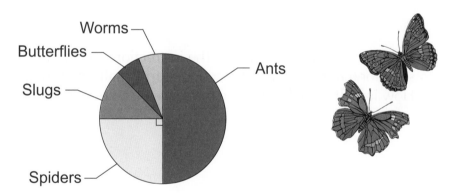

11.   What fraction of the minibeasts found were spiders? Circle the correct option.

      A $^6/_8$ **B** $^4/_8$ **C** $^2/_8$ **D** $^1/_8$ **E** $^5/_8$

Jamal found 4 slugs, 2 butterflies and 2 worms.   Slugs, butterflies and worms make up
the same total fraction of the minibeasts found as the spiders.

12.   How many minibeasts did Jamal find in total?

/ 12

Test 19

Test 20

You have **10 minutes** to do this test. Work as quickly and accurately as you can.

1. A coloured shape has been drawn on the grid below.
    The shape is translated 3 squares to the left and 2 squares up.
    Which letter shows the new position of the shape? Circle the correct option.

    A   **B**   **C**   **D**   **E**

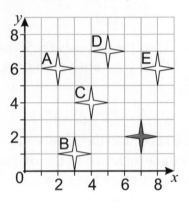

2. Frankie is heating some soup. The instructions say to microwave the
    soup for 6 minutes and 30 seconds, stirring halfway through heating.
    How long should the soup be microwaved before Frankie stirs it?

    ☐ minutes ☐☐ seconds

3. Melanie asks her friends and family what their favourite type of music is.
    She records the results in the table below.

Type of music	Tally
Rock	ⵏⵏ ⵏⵏ I
Pop	ⵏⵏ ⵏⵏ ⵏⵏ
Classical	ⵏⵏ
Jazz	ⵏⵏ ⵏⵏ II

    How many people said their favourite type of music was rock or pop?

    ☐☐

4. The list shows the names and weights of 5 babies born in a hospital on the same day.

Toby	3.7 kg
Lena	2.8 kg
James	4.3 kg
Zoe	3.6 kg
Saida	4.6 kg

A midwife rearranges the list to put the babies in order of weight.
Which baby will be in the middle of the list? Circle the correct option.

A Toby   **C** James   **E** Saida

B Lena   **D** Zoe

A box of Oatiloops contains 600 g of cereal. There are 20 servings in each box.

5. How much does each serving weigh? Circle the correct option.

A 30 g   **B** 40 g   **C** 60 g   **D** 120 g   **E** 300 g

6. One serving of Oatiloops contains 6.1 g of sugar.
How many grams of sugar does 1 box of Oatiloops contain?

 g

7. Which of the following calculations has an answer equal to 450 ml?
Circle the correct option.

A 200 ml + 0.2 l   **C** 3 l + 1.5 l   **E** 1000 ml – 650 ml

B 550 ml – 0.1 l   **D** 200 ml × 4

8. Jayden's book has 864 pages. So far he has read 348 pages.
How many more pages does Jayden need to read before he reaches
the middle of the book?

Kira and Josh each run 100 m at a constant speed.
Kira runs 100 m in 20 seconds. Josh runs 100 m in 30 seconds.

9.   How long did it take Josh to run ⁶/₁₀ of 100 m?

☐☐ seconds

10. How far did Kira run in 7 seconds?
      Circle the correct option.

      A   20 m   **C**   35 m   **E**   65 m
      B   25 m   **D**   50 m

Sasha and Kia are working out their shoe size using the table below.

Length of Foot (cm)	Shoe Size
20.8	4
21.6	5
22.5	6
23.5	7
24.1	8

Sasha's right foot is 21.6 cm in length. Kia's right foot is 1.9 cm longer than Sasha's.

11. How many shoe sizes bigger is Kia's right foot than Sasha's?

☐

12. How many times does the length of Sasha's right foot fit into 1 m?
      Circle the correct option.

      A 8   **B** 7   **C** 6   **D** 5   **E** 4

/ 12

Puzzles 8

Time to practise your **addition** skills with some **bothersome balloons**.

Balloon Bother

Benedict needs to tie weights to his party balloons to keep them from floating away.
Each balloon needs to be tied down by 3 weights, which add up to 30 g.
Write the correct weights underneath each balloon. You must use all the weights.

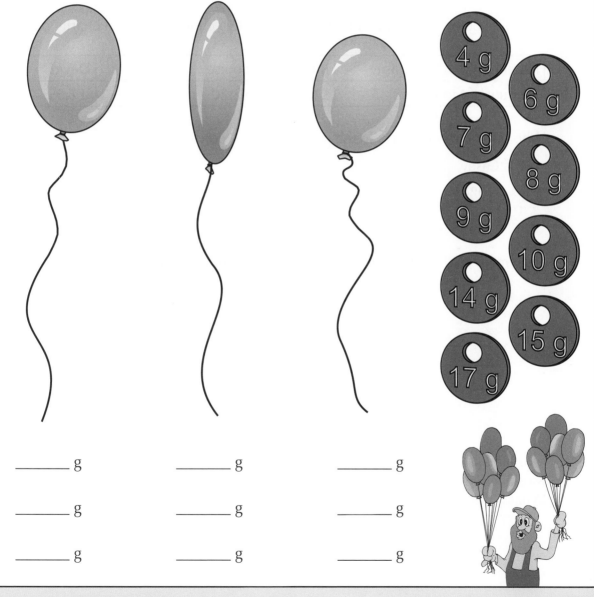

_____ g   _____ g   _____ g

_____ g   _____ g   _____ g

_____ g   _____ g   _____ g

69   Puzzles 8

You have **10 minutes** to do this test. Work as quickly and accurately as you can.

1. Laura is training for a race. She runs 25 km every week for 7 weeks.
    How many kilometres will she run in total?

     km

2. The table below shows the amount of money five children put in a charity pot.

Name	Casey	Kinga	Louise	Hassan	David
Amount of Money	£3.45	£3.60	£2.20	£2.85	£1.95

    Who put the most money in the pot? Circle the correct option.

    A   Casey   **C**   Louise   **E**   David
    B   Kinga   **D**   Hassan

3. How many of these shapes have more than 2 lines of symmetry?

4. Mostafa has a box of 12 pens. Each pen is 10 cm long.
    Mostafa lines up all the pens from end to tip.
    What is the length of the line of pens? Give your answer in m.

    ☐.☐ m

Clara recorded the number of customers in her cafe at different times during the day. The graph below shows her results.

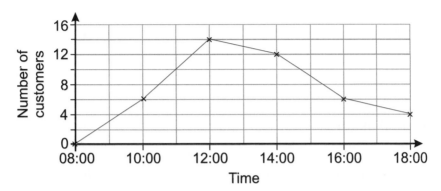

5. How many more customers were in the cafe at 12:00 than at 10:00?

6. How many customers were in the cafe at 4 pm?

7. Duston town band start rehearsing at 19:30. The rehearsal finishes at 20:55. How many minutes long is the rehearsal?

 minutes

8. The ingredients for a pizza are shown below.

    > 1 pizza base
    > 100 ml tomato sauce
    > 1 tomato
    > 150 g of cheese

    John wants to make 10 pizzas. How many kilograms of cheese will he need? Circle the correct option.

    A   15000 kg   **C**   150 kg   **E**   0.15 kg

    B   1500 kg   **D**   1.5 kg

9. Bill thinks of two numbers. He multiplies them together and then subtracts 7.
    The answer he gets is 35. Which two numbers could he have started with?
    Circle the correct option.

    A 6 and 7   **C** 7 and 4   **E** 12 and 3
    B 4 and 8   **D** 5 and 6

Hira has a bag of 60 marbles.

10. Hira divides the marbles into groups of equal sizes.
    Which of the following cannot be the number of groups she has?

    A 2
    B 5
    C 6
    D 9
    E 10

11. $^5/_{12}$ of the marbles are green.
    How many green marbles does Hira have?

12. Jamal is buying cans of cat food.
    The cans are sold in three different multipacks:

12 cans
for £24

6 cans
for £6.60

10 cans
for £12

    Jamal buys two lots of the multipack with the lowest price per can.
    How much does he spend?

    £ ⬚ ⬚ . ⬚ ⬚

/ 12

10

You have **10 minutes** to do this test. Work as quickly and accurately as you can.

1. Write $^4/_{10}$ as a decimal.

2. Raoul has drawn a map of his local park using a coordinate grid.

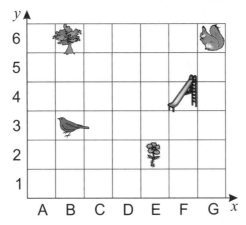

Which of the following can be found in the square F4?
Circle the correct option.

A a tree	**C** a slide	**E** a bird
B a squirrel	**D** a flower	

3. Marcy has 176 songs in her music collection.
    How many songs does Marcy have to the nearest 10?

4. What is XXXVIII + XI? Circle the correct option.

A 28	**C** 49	**E** 37
B 39	**D** 47	

73

5. Which of the following numbers would fit in the box below?
   Circle the correct option.

   576 cm < ?

   A 58 mm   **B** 5.6 m   **C** 570 cm   **D** 640 mm   **E** 6 m

This pictogram shows the number of cars sold in 1 month by members of a sales team.

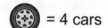 = 4 cars

6. How many cars did the team sell in total?

7. Each team member earns an extra £100 per car that they sell.
   How much extra money did the team member who sold the most cars make?

   £

8. The scales show the weight of 3 identical textbooks.
   What is the weight of 1 textbook?
   Circle the correct option.

   A 0.3 kg
   B 2 kg
   C 3 kg
   D 1.2 kg
   E 1.3 kg

9. Lucy has bought some new clothes. Her receipt is shown below.

RECEIPT
Coat   £66.00
Shoes £25.40
Scarf   £4.99

How much has Lucy spent in total?

£

Harris buys boxes of baseball caps to sell in his hat shop.
There are 5 red caps, 7 blue caps and 8 black caps in each box.

10. Harris wants 70 black caps to sell in his shop.
     What is the lowest number of boxes he will need to buy?

11. What fraction of the caps in each box are red?
     Circle the correct option.

     A   ¹/₃
     B   ¹/₄
     C   ¹/₅
     D   ¹/₆
     E   ¹/₇

12. Harris pays £40 for one box of baseball caps.
     He sells each cap for £4.50.
     How much profit does Harris make on each cap?

£

/ 12

Test 23

You have **10 minutes** to do this test. Work as quickly and accurately as you can.

1. Karen and Phil are playing an arcade game.
    Phil scores 1385 points. Karen scores 1000 more points than Phil.
    How many points does Karen score?

Mason records how many text messages he receives each day for five days.
His results are shown in the table.

Day	Monday	Tuesday	Wednesday	Thursday	Friday
Tally	|||| |||| ||	||||		||||	||||	||||			

2. How many more texts did Mason receive on Monday than on Thursday?

3. Which of the following statements is true? Circle the correct option.

    A Mason received the most texts on Friday.

    B Mason didn't receive more than 8 text messages on any day.

    C In total, Mason received less than 30 text messages.

    D Mason received 34 text messages in total.

    E The total number of text messages he received is a multiple of 6.

4. Which of these arrows is pointing to $^{11}/_{100}$?
    Circle the correct option.

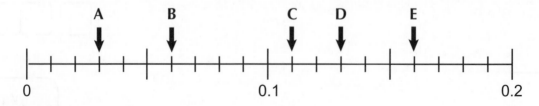

5. Mr McCafferty buys 7 packs of straws for a class art project.
Each pack contains 124 straws. How many straws does he have in total?

Tamsin and Greg are sharing a bottle of juice.

6. Tamsin drinks $^5/_9$ of the bottle and Greg drinks $^2/_9$ of the bottle.
How much juice is left in total? Give your answer as a fraction.

7. The bottles of juice can be bought in packs of 6.
Each bottle contains 200 ml of juice.
What is the total amount of juice in one pack? Give your answer in litres.

 litres

8. Ayesha plots a quadrilateral
on the coordinate grid to the right.
She plots these points:
(4, 2) (2, 5) (4, 7) (6, 5)

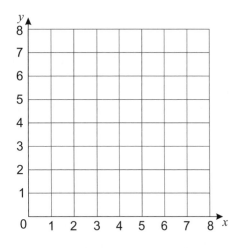

What shape does Ayesha plot? Circle the correct option.

A

B

C

D

E

77

9. Sheana has a sheet of fabric that is 2 m long and 1 m wide.
    She cuts the sheet into quarters, as shown below.

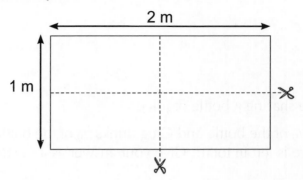

2 m

1 m

What is the perimeter of one of the quarters? Circle the correct option.

A   2.5 m   **C**   4 m   **E**   3 m
B   6 m   **D**   5.5 m

10. Giles buys 1 pencil case and four pens for £6.50.
    The pencil case costs £3.70. What is the price of one pen?

£

Zoe is watching a documentary. The documentary is 2 hours and 30 minutes long.

11. Zoe started watching the documentary at 7:25 pm. At what time will it finish?
    Give your answer using the 24-hour clock.

12. Zoe has watched $^1/_5$ of the documentary so far.
    How many minutes of the documentary has she watched?

minutes

/ 12

Have a go at these puzzles. They'll help you to improve your **counting** skills.

Dotty Drawing

Calvin the caterpillar likes to count in multiples of 25.

Complete the picture of his favourite food, by drawing lines between the dots.

The dots must be connected in order, starting with number 25.

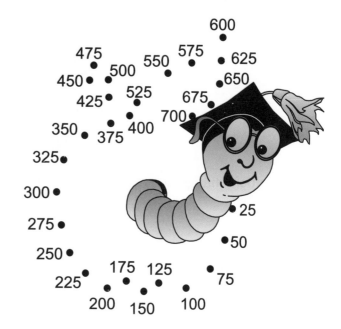

Fussy Fish

The fish below only eat fish food shapes with the correct number of sides. The number on each fish shows how many sides its food shapes need to have. Draw lines to match each fish with the correct fish food shape.

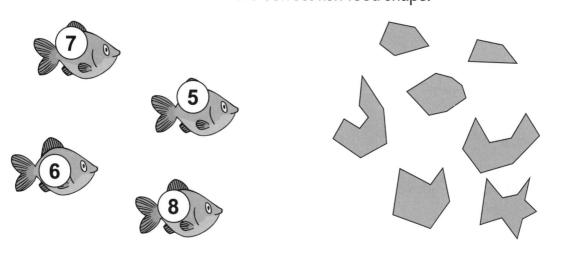

You have **10 minutes** to do this test. Work as quickly and accurately as you can.

1. The coins in Sasha's purse are shown below.

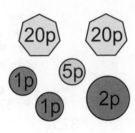

How much change does Sasha have to the nearest 10p?

 p

2. George has 26 DVDs. Larry has double the number of DVDs that George has.
    How many DVDs does Larry have?

Renée is painting the star decoration shown below. She has painted 1 section blue.

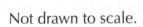

Not drawn to scale.

3. Renée paints 4 more sections of the star blue. What fraction of the star will
    be painted blue once Renée has finished? Circle the correct option.

    A $^3/_{10}$ **C** $^5/_{10}$ **E** $^7/_{10}$
    B $^4/_{10}$ **D** $^6/_{10}$

4. All the star's sides are the same length. What is the perimeter of the star?

    cm

5. Which of the following calculations is incorrect? Circle the correct option.

    A $9 \times 4 = 36$

    B $28 \div 7 = 4$

    C $7 \times 5 = 35$

    D $81 \div 9 = 9$

    E $11 \times 12 = 131$

6. The temperature in Sai's conservatory is 20.5 °C.
    The temperature increases by 0.5 °C every hour for the next 4 hours.
    What is the temperature in Sai's conservatory after 4 hours?

 °C

7. Dean feeds his dog 330 g of dog food per day. He splits the food into 3 meals.
    The first meal contains 130 g of food. The rest of the food is split equally between
    the second and third meal. How much food should the dog get in the third meal?

 g

8. Nathan buys 6 sausages for £1.80. Carrie buys 8 sausages for £3.20.
    How much more has Carrie spent per sausage than Nathan?
    Circle the correct option.

    A   10p   **C**   30p   **E**   50p

    B   20p   **D**   40p

9. Nina has a paper shape.
    It has an even number of sides and 1 line of symmetry.
    Which of these could be Nina's shape? Circle the correct option.

 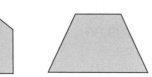 

    A   **B**   **C**   **D**   **E**

Test 24

10. David arrives in Berlin at 18:00 on Tuesday. He stays in the city for 36 hours. When does David leave Berlin? Circle the correct option.

    A   18:00 on Wednesday

    B   06:00 on Wednesday

    C   06:00 on Thursday

    D   12:00 on Thursday

    E   18:00 on Thursday

The bar chart below shows the numbers of different types of racket sold by a sports shop in one week. The bar for squash rackets is missing.

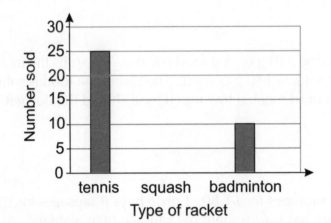

11. The shop sold 5 times as many tennis rackets as squash rackets. How many squash rackets did it sell?

12. Badminton rackets are sold for £29.90 each. How much money was made from selling the badminton rackets in total? Circle the correct option.

    A   £290.00   **C**   £299.99   **E**   £2999.99

    B   £299.00   **D**   £2999.00

/ 12

You have **10 minutes** to do this test. Work as quickly and accurately as you can.

1. Ed buys 7 boxes of cereal bars. Each box contains 6 cereal bars.
    How many cereal bars has Ed bought?

2. An incomplete calculation is shown below.

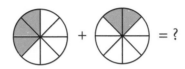

Which of the following is the correct answer to the calculation above?
Circle the correct option.

   A $^1/_2$
   B $^1/_4$
   C $^2/_8$
   D $^5/_8$
   E $^8/_{16}$

3. A real double decker bus is about 4 m tall.
    A toy double decker bus is 100 times smaller.
    How many metres tall is the toy double decker bus?

4. A full set of football stickers contains 120 stickers.
    Ellie has 99 stickers. Ryan gives Ellie 11 new stickers for her collection.
    How many more stickers does Ellie need for a full set?

5.   The grid below shows a plan of Rochelle's bedroom. The floor is covered with carpet tiles. Rochelle wants to replace the carpet tiles in the shaded area.

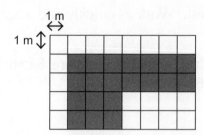

1 m ↔

1 m ↕

The tiles she wants to use each measure 1 m by 1 m. Each tile costs £4.
How much will the tiles that Rochelle is replacing cost in total?

£ ☐☐

The weights of 4 fish caught in a fishing competition are shown in the table.

Type of fish	Weight in kg
Carp	2.1 kg
Brown trout	0.8 kg
Rainbow trout	1.5 kg
Chub	2.3 kg

6.   What is the difference in weight between the heaviest fish and the lightest fish?

☐.☐ kg

7.   What is the weight of the carp in grams? Circle the correct option.

    A   0.21 g   C   210 g   E   21000 g
    B   21 g   D   2100 g

8.   600 people pass through a train station in 1 hour.
      $^6/_{10}$ of those people are travelling to or from work.
      How many people passing through the station are travelling to or from work?

☐☐☐

The table below allows you to convert between miles and kilometres.

Distance in miles	Distance in kilometres
1.0	1.6
2.0	3.2
3.0	4.8
4.0	6.4
5.0	8.0

9. Zofia lives 6.4 km away from her grandma's house.
   How many miles does Zofia live from her grandma's house?

   ☐.☐ miles

10. Keiran goes on a 10 mile bike ride.
    What is this distance in kilometres?

    ☐☐ km

11. Alex drives 2.5 miles to work.
    Which of the following is the best estimate of this distance in km?
    Circle the correct option.

    A   3.0 km
    B   3.2 km
    C   3.6 km
    D   4.0 km
    E   4.4 km

12. 8 apples and 6 oranges cost £4.50. 1 orange costs 35p.
    How much does 1 apple cost?

    ☐☐ p

    / 12

Test 25

Puzzles 10

Time for a puzzle. This one's a fun way to practise **multiplication** and **division**.

Smart Art

A gallery is having an art exhibition. Each artist has a number.
So does each piece of art.

When you multiply the numbers on the correct 2 pieces of art together,
you get the number of the artist that made them.

Draw lines to match each artist to the correct two pieces of art.

You have **10 minutes** to do this test. Work as quickly and accurately as you can.

1. What number is the arrow pointing to?

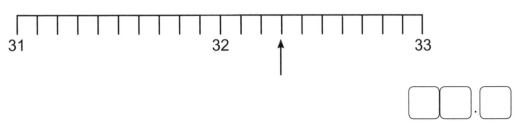

☐☐.☐

2. The clock below shows how long a football match has been played for.
   Half-time is exactly 45 minutes into the match.

   How long is it until half-time?

   ☐☐ minutes and ☐☐ seconds

3. Team A has 47 supporters at the football match.
   Team B has 56 supporters at the football match.
   How many supporters are at the match?

   ☐☐☐

4. A pattern is shown on the right. Which of these statements is true?
   Circle the correct option.

   A The pattern is made up of pentagons only.
   B The pattern is made up of a pentagon and 5 hexagons.
   C The pattern is made up of a pentagon and 5 quadrilaterals.
   D The pattern is made up of a hexagon and 5 pentagons.
   E The pattern is made up of a hexagon and 5 quadrilaterals.

Aisha spends £300 on 12 boxes of fairy lights and a Christmas tree.
The Christmas tree cost £60.

5. How much did each box of fairy lights cost?

£

6. Aisha also buys a box of baubles.
    She pays $^1/_{10}$ of the price of the Christmas tree for it.
    How much does the box of baubles cost?

£ ☐

The bar chart shows the running time of 4 different films.

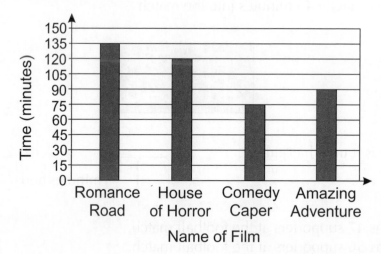

7. What is the difference in length between the longest film and the shortest film?
    Circle the correct option.

    A   60 minutes   **C**   30 minutes   **E**   Cannot tell.
    B   45 minutes   **D**   15 minutes

8. Romance Road starts at 20:05 at the cinema. What time will it finish?
    Circle the correct option.

    A   22:05   **C**   22:35   **E**   22:55
    B   22:20   **D**   22:40

9. The Romans first invaded Britain in the year 55 B.C.
   Which of the following shows the number 55 in Roman numerals?
   Circle the correct option.

   A   XXXXV   **C**   VL   **E**   VV
   B   CV   **D**   LV

Caleb is building towers with wooden blocks.
He builds each tower by stacking one block on top of the other.
Each block is 4 cm high and weighs 6 g.

10. Caleb builds one tower that is 1 m high.
    How much does the tower weigh?

    ☐☐☐ g

11. Caleb builds another tower that weighs 120 g.
    How tall is this tower? Give your answer in cm.

    ☐☐☐ cm

12. The diagram below shows the plan view of a house and garden.
    The area of the garden is $^1/_3$ of the area of the house.

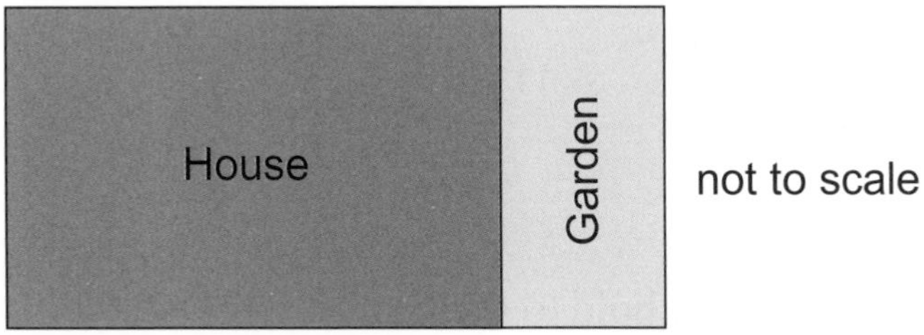

    House   Garden   not to scale

    The area of the garden is 45 m².
    What is the total area of the house and the garden?

    ☐☐☐ m²

    / 12

Test 26

You have **10 minutes** to do this test. Work as quickly and accurately as you can.

1. There are 63 people at a wedding reception and 9 tables. If the same number of people sit at each table, how many guests should there be per table?

2. The picture below shows a girl and a tree.

The girl is 1 m tall.
Which of the following is the best estimate of the height of the tree?
Circle the correct option.

   A   3 m   **C**   13 m   **E**   18 m
   B   7 m   **D**   15 m

3. A bucket holds 7668 ml of water.
   How much water does the bucket hold to the nearest litre?

   litres

4. Kylie thinks of a number. She counts backwards in 3s until she gets to –5.
   Which of these could have been her original number? Circle the correct option.

   A   –1   **C**   6   **E**   9
   B   3   **D**   7

The number of pupils at each of 6 secondary schools is shown below.

| 1206 | 828 | 1392 | 965 | 1839 | 978 |

5. How many pupils do the 2 schools with the highest number of pupils have in total?

6. To the nearest hundred, how many pupils attend the school with the smallest number of pupils?

7. Jacob is cutting out pastry circles to make jam tarts.
He can cut 8 circles out of each sheet of pastry.
How many sheets of pastry will Jacob need to make 55 jam tarts?

8. Hamish orders a computer game from the USA. He places the order on Tuesday the 8th of May. The game takes exactly 2 weeks to arrive.
On what date does Hamish receive the game? Circle the correct option.

   A   15th of May
   B   20th of May
   C   22nd of May
   D   24th of May
   E   2nd of June

9. Esme leaves home at 2 pm. She spends 15 minutes walking to the train station. She waits for 5 minutes and then gets on a train. The train arrives at Esme's destination at 3:10 pm. How long was Esme's train journey?

minutes

10. The shape below is rotated by $^{1}/_{4}$ turn anti-clockwise.

Which of these shows the final position of the shape? Circle the correct option.

A   **B**   **C**   **D**   **E**

The graph below shows how the value of a car changes over time.

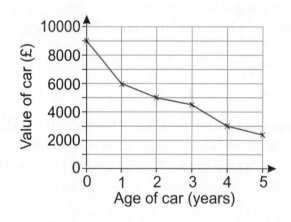

11. By how much does the value of the car drop between 0 and 1 years of age?

£ ☐☐☐☐

12. Niamh buys the car when it is 2 years old.
Niamh pays $^{4}/_{5}$ of the value price. Her father pays for the rest.
How much does Niamh pay? Circle the correct option.

    A £1000   **C** £3000   **E** £5000
    B £2000   **D** £4000

/ 12

You have **10 minutes** to do this test. Work as quickly and accurately as you can.

1.   What is 554 + 336?

Bashar takes ⁴/₁₀ of a cake.

2.   What is ⁴/₁₀ as a decimal? Circle the correct option.

    A   0.44   **C**   0.4   **E**   4.4

    B   0.04   **D**   4.0

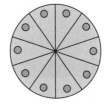

3.   Which of these is equivalent to the fraction of cake left over once
      Bashar has taken his share? Circle the correct option.

      A   ²/₅   **C**   ²/₃   **E**   ¹/₆

      B   ³/₅   **D**   ¹/₄

4.   Preeti is making a fruit pie.
      She has 400 g of strawberries, 250 g of raspberries and 125 g of blueberries.
      How many grams of blackberries does Preeti need so that she has 1 kg of fruit?

g

5.   Which of these shapes has a perimeter of 28 cm?
      Circle the correct option.

                          Not drawn to scale.

4 cm [4 cm]   [6 cm 8 cm]   [10 cm 3 cm]   3 cm [5 cm 8 cm 4 cm 6 cm]   5 cm [5 cm 5 cm]

        A   **B**   **C**   **D**   **E**

The grid below shows a series of shapes.

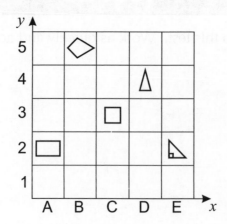

6. In which square is the kite? Circle the correct option.

    A   (A1)   **C**   (C3)   **E**   (E2)
    B   (B5)   **D**   (D4)

7. Which of the following describes a route from the right-angled triangle to the isosceles triangle? Circle the correct option.

    A   2 down, 1 right   **C**   1 left, 2 up   **E**   3 up, 1 left
    B   2 up, 1 right   **D**   2 left, 1 up

8. Devan pays £5.00 for a comic and 5 gobstopper sweets. The comic cost £2.50.
    How much did each gobstopper sweet cost? Give your answer in pence.

9. A chocolate bar costs 75p.
    If Eric has £3.40, how many chocolate bars can he buy?

Hannah counted the number of different birds in her garden one Saturday.
She drew the pictogram below but forgot to include a key.

Type of bird	Number
House sparrow	⬤ ⬤ ⬤ ⬤ ⬤
Starling	⬤ ⬤ ◗
Blackbird	⬤ ◗
Robin	◗

Hannah saw 20 house sparrows and 10 starlings.

10. How many birds does each full symbol represent? Circle the correct option.

    A 1   **B** 2   **C** 3   **D** 4   **E** 5

11. How many robins did Hannah see in her garden?

12. The table below shows how much money went in and out of Ollie's bank
account between the 12th of January 2017 and the 28th of January 2017.

Date	Money In	Money Out
12 / 01 / 2017		£5.53
21 / 01 / 2017	£10.00	
28 / 01 / 2017		£2.99

At the start of the day on the 12th of January 2017, Ollie has £20.00 in his account.
How much does Ollie have in his bank account by the end of the day
on the 28th of January 2017?

/ 12

More Puzzles! Here's a chance to practise **problem-solving** and **Roman numerals**.

Queenly Conundrum

The Queen is having a dinner party but the guests are being awkward about where they sit. Use the information below to work out where to put the Duke, Princess Zoe, the Countess and Prince Paul at the dinner table.

> The Duke says: *"I will not sit next to the Countess or Prince Paul."*
> Princess Zoe says: *"I want to sit opposite Prince Paul."*
> The Countess says: *"I want to sit next to the Queen, on her right-hand side."*

Write the person's name in the box where they should sit.

The Queen

Shy Romans

Some Roman soldiers are hiding behind this shield.
Add up the answers to the 4 calculations below
to find out how many there are.

I + II = _____   V + III = _____

X + V = _____   X – IV = _____

Number of Roman soldiers hiding = _____

You have **10 minutes** to do this test. Work as quickly and accurately as you can.

Sierra makes the shape below from some squares. Each square is 1 cm².

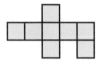

1. Which of the following shapes has the same area as Sierra's shape?
    Circle the correct option.

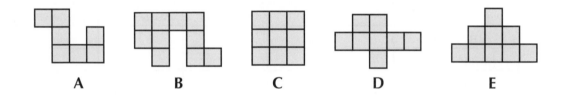

| A | B | C | D | E |

2. The squares have sides that are each 1 cm long.
    What is the perimeter of Sierra's shape?

 cm

3. 5 different vehicles and their heights are shown below.
    Which of the vehicles is the tallest? Circle the correct option.

| 385 cm | 310 cm | 295 cm | 198 cm | 395 cm |
| A | B | C | D | E |

Siobhan is at a theme park.

4. She goes on a ride which is 62.4 m tall.
    What is the height of the ride to the nearest metre?

    ⬚⬚ m

5. Siobhan joins the queue for a ride at 10:37. She queues for $^1/_4$ of an hour.
    What time does Siobhan get on the ride?

    ⬚⬚:⬚⬚

Jessica picks 5 possible activities for her birthday.
She asks 3 friends to score each activity out of 5.
The results are shown in the table below.

	Theatre	Zoo	Cinema	Aquarium	Museum
Amy	3	2	4	1	5
James	1	3	5	2	4
Rajesh	3	4	5	2	1

6. Which activity had the second highest total score?
    Circle the correct option.

    A   Theatre   C   Cinema   E   Museum
    B   Zoo   D   Aquarium

7. Jessica buys 4 tickets for her birthday activity. They cost £32.40 in total.
    How much did each individual ticket cost?

    £⬚⬚.⬚⬚

8. Donna needs 1200 g of wool to knit a jumper. If there are 250 g of wool in each
    ball of wool, how many balls of wool does she need to buy?

    ⬚

9. A ferry is travelling from England to France.
    $^{13}/_{100}$ of the passengers are from Hampshire. $^{15}/_{100}$ of the passengers are from Kent.
    What fraction of passengers are from either Hampshire or Kent?
    Circle the correct option.

    A $^{14}/_{100}$ **B** $^{29}/_{100}$ **C** $^{18}/_{50}$ **D** $^{28}/_{200}$ **E** $^{28}/_{100}$

10. Jude goes to the shop to buy 6 new pens. Each pen normally costs £1.
    The shop has an offer on pens, so Jude can buy 6 pens for £4.80.
    Which of the following could be the offer? Circle the correct option.

    A Buy 1 pen and get 1 pen free.

    B 20p off every pen.

    C 3 pens for the price of 2 pens.

    D $^{1}/_{10}$ of the price off every pen.

    E Buy 1 pen and get a second pen half price.

The pictogram below shows how many tennis matches 5 different tennis players have won in their last 30 matches.

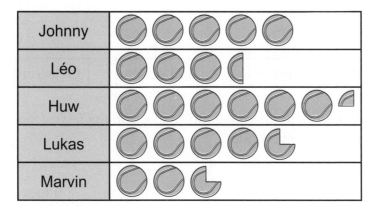

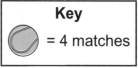

Key

= 4 matches

11. Which player has won 19 out of 30 matches? Circle the correct option.

    A Johnny   **B** Léo   **C** Huw   **D** Lukas   **E** Marvin

12. Tennis matches cannot end in a draw.
    How many of his last 30 matches has Marvin lost?

/ 12

You have **10 minutes** to do this test. Work as quickly and accurately as you can.

1. In which of the following numbers has the digit in the tens column been underlined?
    Circle the correct option.

    A   1̲097.0   **B**   65̲4.2   **C**   8.5̲3   **D**   2727̲.8   **E**   2̲43.1

2. Jasper gets a part-time job at a coffee shop over the summer holidays.
    He works 12 hours a week for 5 weeks.
    How many hours does Jasper work at the coffee shop over the summer?

    ☐☐ hours

Patty has 5 cards, which are shown below.

| Hexagon | Triangle | Pentagon | Trapezium | Octagon |

3. Patty puts the cards in order, from the name of the shape with the fewest sides
    to the name of the shape with the most sides.
    What is the correct order? Circle the correct option.

A	Pentagon	Triangle	Hexagon	Octagon	Trapezium
B	Trapezium	Triangle	Pentagon	Hexagon	Octagon
C	Triangle	Trapezium	Pentagon	Hexagon	Octagon
D	Pentagon	Triangle	Hexagon	Octagon	Trapezium
E	Triangle	Trapezium	Hexagon	Pentagon	Octagon

4. Patty adds up the total number of sides of all 5 shapes.
    What is the total number of sides?

    ☐☐

Jason measures the heights of his 4 children.
The height of each child is shown on the bar chart below.

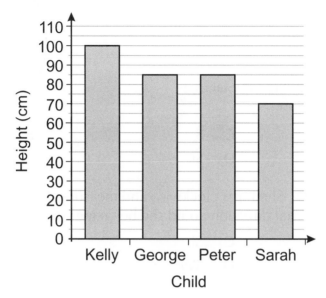

5. How many centimetres taller than Sarah is Kelly?

 cm

6. How tall is Peter in m?

 m

7. A soap dispenser dispenses 2 ml of soap each time it is used.
So far 48 ml of soap have been dispensed.
How many times has the soap dispenser been used?

8. Philippa pays £670 per month in rent.
How much does she spend on rent in 3 months?

£

9. Anushka stands in one spot. She is facing north (N).
   She makes the following turns.

   - $^1/_4$ turn clockwise,
   - $^1/_2$ turn anticlockwise,
   - $^3/_4$ turn clockwise.

   What direction is Anushka now facing?
   Circle the correct option.

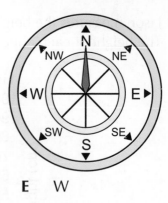

   A NW   **C** S   **E** W

   B E   **D** SE

10. Anushka faces east (E). She turns clockwise and measures the angle of her turn.
    The angle is acute. What direction could she be facing? Circle the correct option.

    A NE   **C** SE   **E** S

    B N   **D** SW

Beachcastle School and Ampleton School are competing in a netball match.

11. The netball court is shown below.

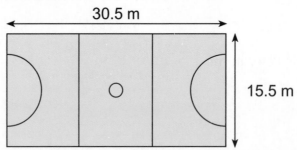

    As part of their warm up, the players run around the edge of the netball court twice.
    How many metres do they run?

    ⬚⬚⬚ m

12. Pupils from both schools are watching the match.
    74 of the pupils are from Ampleton School.
    84 of the pupils are girls. 40 of the girls are from Beachcastle School.
    How many boys are from Ampleton School?

    ⬚⬚

    / 12

You have **10 minutes** to do this test. Work as quickly and accurately as you can.

Herbert picks some daffodils and daisies from his garden.

1. Herbert picks 9 daffodils. Each daffodil has 6 petals.
   How many daffodil petals are there in total?

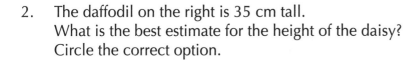

2. The daffodil on the right is 35 cm tall.
   What is the best estimate for the height of the daisy?
   Circle the correct option.

   A   12 cm

   B   4 cm

   C   15 cm

   D   7 cm

   E   2 cm

Perez has 3 homework projects. The length of each project is shown below.

Project 1:	9 pages
Project 2:	4 pages
Project 3:	11 pages

3. Perez has 156 sheets of paper in his printer. He prints off all 3 projects.
   1 page is printed on each sheet of paper.
   How many sheets of paper are left in his printer?

4. Project 1 contains 1387 words. Project 2 contains 1250 words.
   How many more words are in Project 1 than Project 2?

Elliott is flying to Florida for a holiday in 3 weeks and 4 days.

5.   How many days is it until Elliott goes on holiday?

6.   The airline has a weight limit of 23.0 kg for baggage. Elliott's suitcase and its
     contents must not weigh more than this. Elliott's suitcase weighs 4.6 kg.
     What is the maximum weight of belongings that Elliott can pack?

kg

Geeta is selling scented candles at a village fair.
She records how many of each type of candle she sells in a tally chart.

Candle scent	Tally
Cinnamon	ＩＨＴ ＩＨＴ ＩＩ
Strawberry	ＩＨＴ ＩＨＴ ＩＩＩＩ
Rose	ＩＨＴ ＩＩ
Vanilla	ＩＨＴ ＩＩＩＩ
Gingerbread	ＩＨＴ ＩＨＴ ＩＩＩ
Lavender	ＩＨＴ

7.   How many vanilla candles and gingerbread candles has Geeta sold in total?

8.   How many more strawberry candles has Geeta sold than rose candles?

9.   What fraction of the candles sold were cinnamon scented?
     Circle the correct option.

     A $^{11}/_{60}$ B $^{12}/_{60}$ C $^{12}/_{40}$ D $^{12}/_{50}$ E $^{11}/_{50}$

10. Ticket prices for an activity centre are shown below.

Adult ticket	£9.50
Child ticket	£8.00
Family saver ticket (2 adults and 2 children)	£30.00

There are 5 adults and 5 children going to the activity centre.
What is the cheapest possible total price for their tickets? Circle the correct option.

A   £82.50   **B**   £69.50   **C**   £77.50   **D**   £87.50   **E**   £90.00

A shape and a cross have been drawn on the grid below.

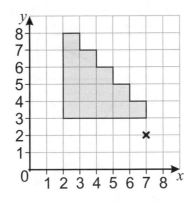

11. Which of the following sets of coordinates represents a point inside the shape?
Circle the correct option.

A   (4, 5)   **B**   (3, 2)   **C**   (7, 1)   **D**   (8, 5)   **E**   (5, 7)

12. The cross has the coordinates (7, 2). It is translated so that it sits inside the shape.
Which of the following could be the translation? Circle the correct answer.

A   1 square right and 2 squares up.

B   1 square left and 4 squares up.

C   2 squares left and 2 squares down.

D   4 squares left and 4 squares up.

E   6 squares left and 2 squares up.

/ 12

Time for a break! This puzzle is perfect for practising your **4**, **6** and **7** times tables.

Pet Portrait

Patricia wants to have a framed picture of her pet.
To help Patricia get her picture, shade in:

- all of the squares and rectangles containing multiples of 7.
- all of the triangles containing multiples of 4 or 6.

M4XPDE1